ROCK
& POP

Grade 2
C000229040

ROCK
& POP

TRINITY
COLLEGE LONDON

THE EXAM AT A GLANCE

For your Rock & Pop exam you will need to perform a set of **three songs** and one of the **Session skills** assessments, either **Playback** or **Improvising**. You can choose the order in which you play your set-list.

Song 1

Choose a song from this book

OR from www.trinityrock.com

Song 2

Choose a different song from this book

OR from www.trinityrock.com

OR perform a song you have chosen yourself: this could be your own cover version or a song you have written. It should be at the same level as the songs in this book. See the website for detailed requirements.

Song 3: Technical focus

Choose one of the Technical focus songs from this book, which cover three specific technical elements.

Session skills

Choose either **Playback** or **Improvising**.

When you are preparing for your exam please check on **www.trinityrock.com** for the most up-to-date information and requirements as these can change from time to time.

CONTENTS

Songs	I Love Rock 'n' Roll	4
	2, 4, 6, 8 Motorway	6
	Rock Around The Clock	8
	Pretty Vacant	10
Technical focus songs	The Modern Age	13
	Mean Jumper Blues	17
About the songs	I Love Rock 'n' Roll	20
	2, 4, 6, 8 Motorway	21
	Rock Around The Clock	22
	Pretty Vacant	23
	The Modern Age	24
	Mean Jumper Blues	25
Session skills	Playback	26
	Improvising	28
Help pages	Choosing a song for your exam	29
	Writing your own song	30
	Playing in a band	31
	Playing with backing tracks	32
	Copyright in a song	32

Tuning track: E, A, D, G, B, E with a pause between each note.

Trinity College London's Rock & Pop syllabus and supporting publications have been devised and produced in association with Faber Music and Peters Edition London.

Published by:
Trinity College London
www.trinitycollege.com

Registered in the UK. Company no. 02683033
Charity no. 1014792
Patron HRH The Duke of Kent KG

First published in 2012 by Trinity College London

Third impression, October 2014

Cover and book design by Chloë Alexander
Brand development by Andy Ashburner @ Caffeinehit (www.caffeinehit.com)
Photographs courtesy of Rex Features Limited.
Printed in England by Caligraving Ltd

Audio produced, mixed and mastered by Tom Fleming
Guitar arranged by Tom Fleming
Backing tracks arranged by Tom Fleming
Musicians
Vocals: Bo Walton, Brendan Reilly & Alison Symons
Keyboards: Oliver Weeks
Guitar: Tom Fleming
Bass: Ben Hillyard
Drums: George Double
Studio Engineer: Joel Davies www.thelimehouse.com

ISBN: 978-0-85736-220-9

SONGS I LOVE ROCK 'N' ROLL

Joan Jett And The Blackhearts

Words and Music by Alan Merrill and Jake Hooker

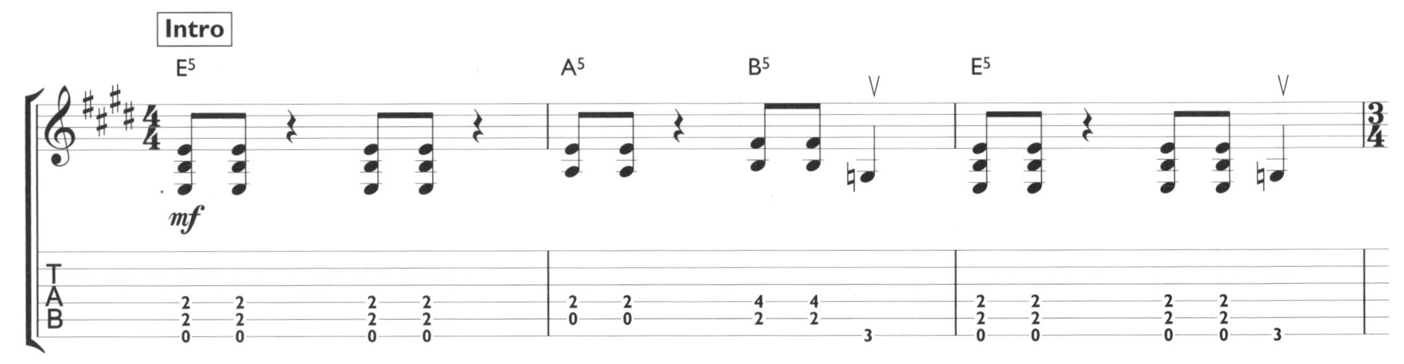

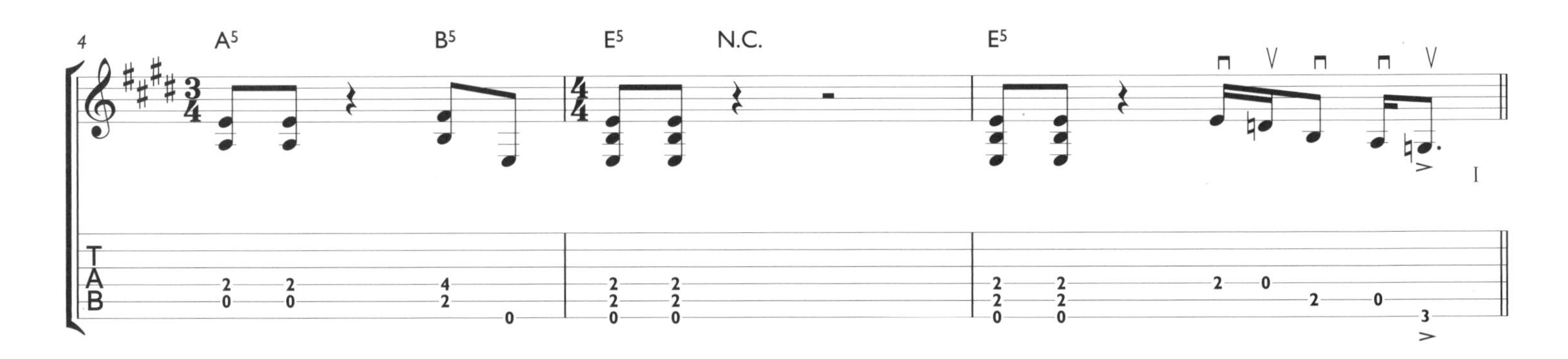

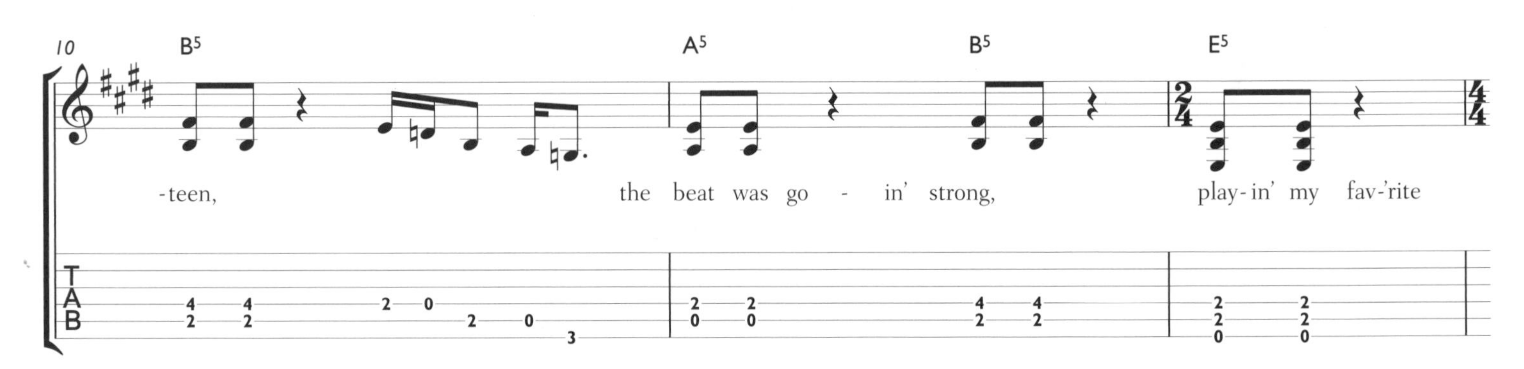

13
A5
N.C.
song. And I could tell it wouldn't be long 'til he was with me, yeah, me, and I could

16
B5
tell it wouldn't be long 'til he was with me, yeah, me, sing - in'...

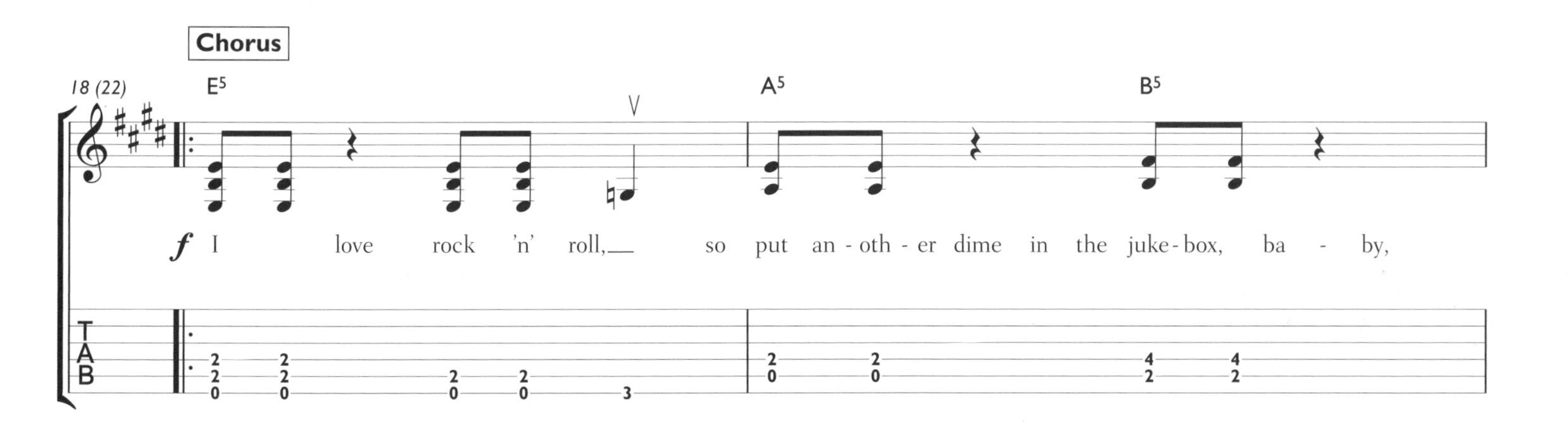
Chorus
18 (22)
E5
A5
B5
f I love rock 'n' roll, so put an - oth - er dime in the juke - box, ba - by,

20 (24)
E5
A5
B5
E5
I love rock 'n' roll, so come and take your time and dance with... me.

SONGS 2,4,6,8 MOTORWAY

Tom Robinson Band
Words and Music by Tom Robinson

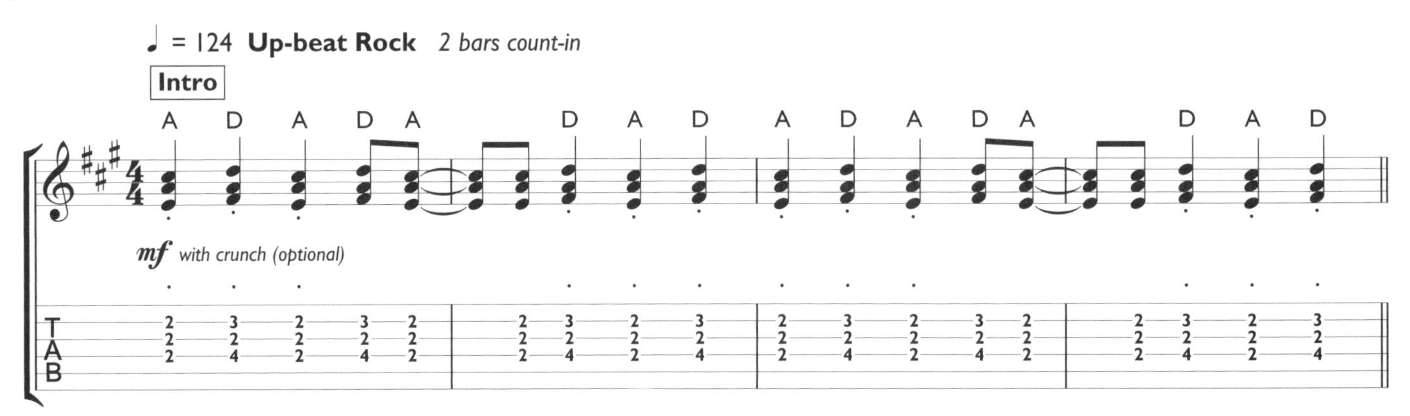

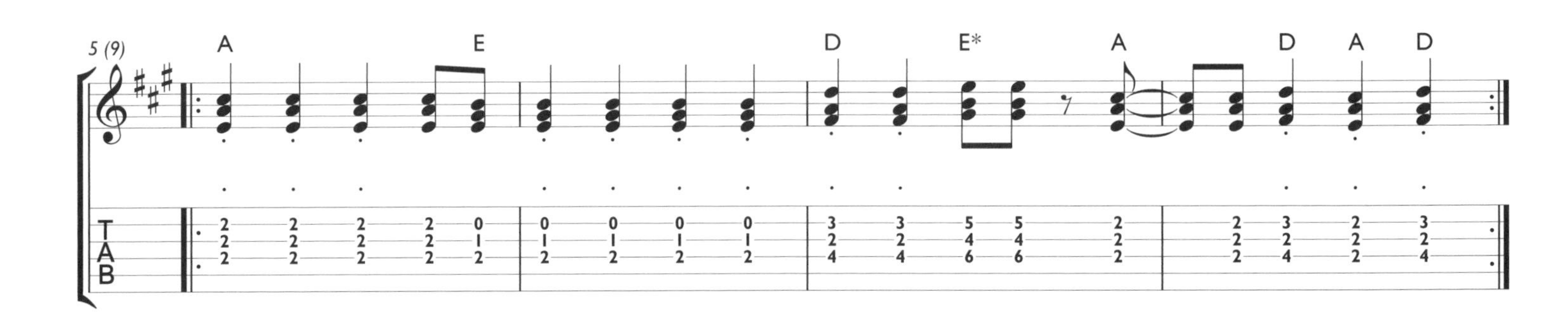

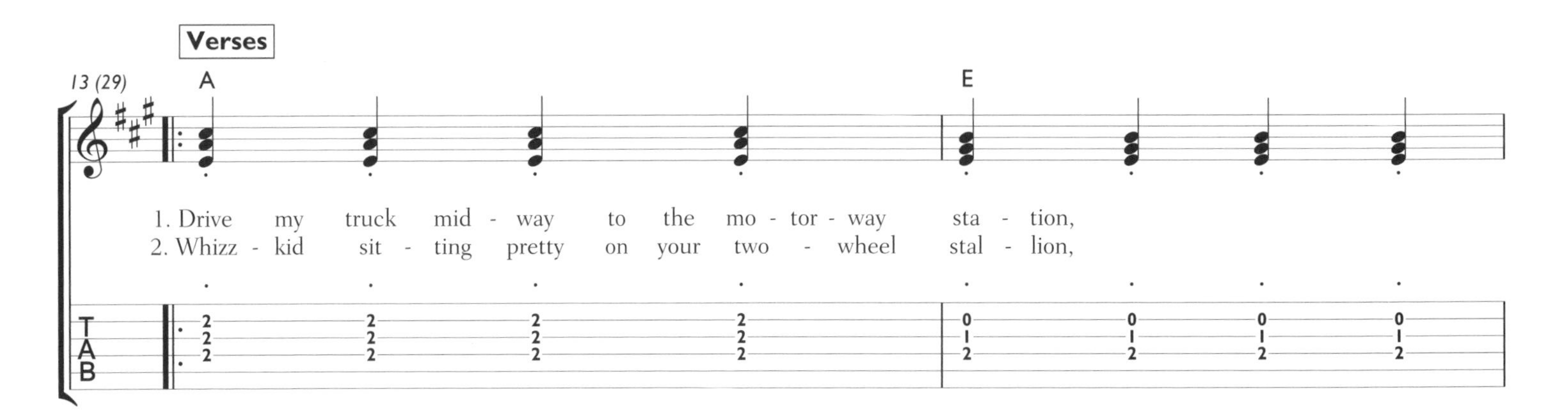

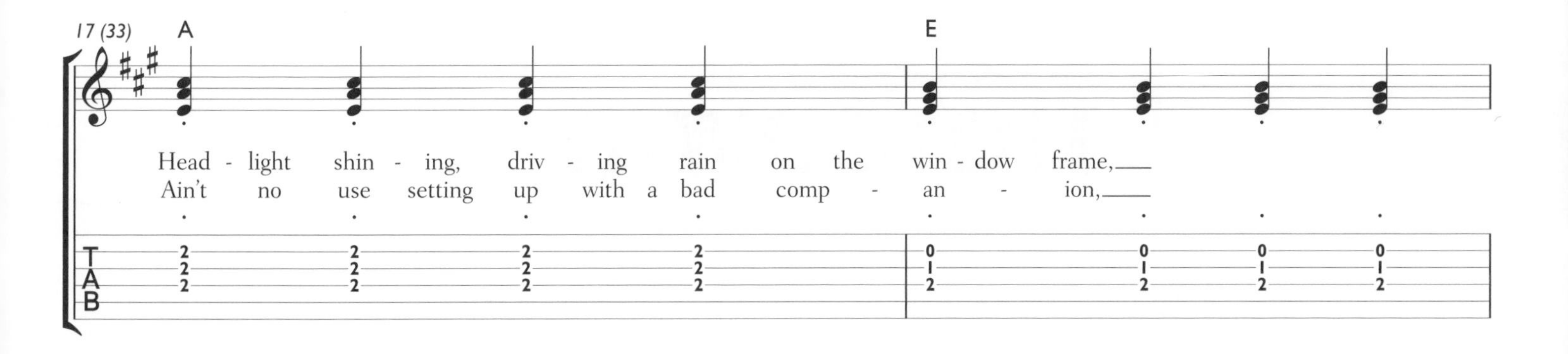
17 (33)
A
E
Head - light shin - ing, driv - ing rain on the win - dow frame,
Ain't no use setting up with a bad comp - an - ion,
T
A
B

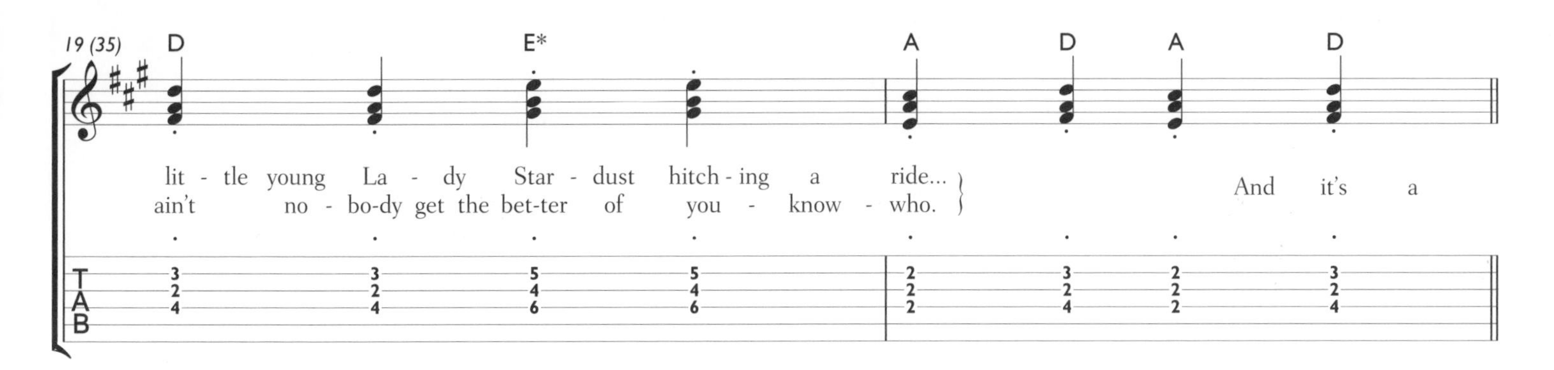
19 (35)
D
E*
A
D
A
D
lit - tle young La - dy Star - dust hitch - ing a ride...
ain't no - bo-dy get the bet-ter of you - know - who.
And it's a
T
A
B

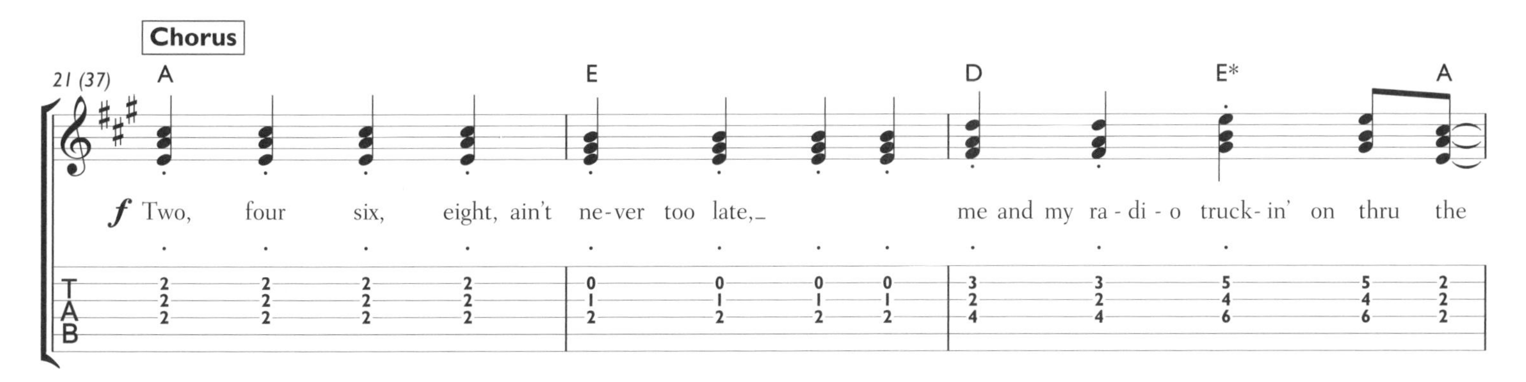
Chorus
21 (37)
A
E
D
E*
A
f
Two, four six, eight, ain't ne-ver too late,
me and my ra - di - o truck- in' on thru the
T
A
B

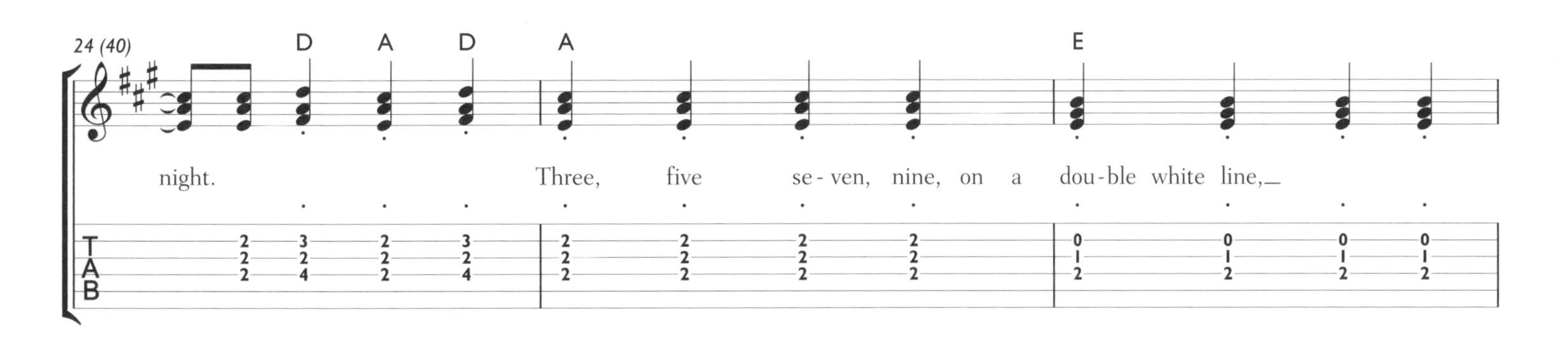
24 (40)
D
A
D
A
E
night.
Three, five se - ven, nine, on a dou - ble white line,
T
A
B

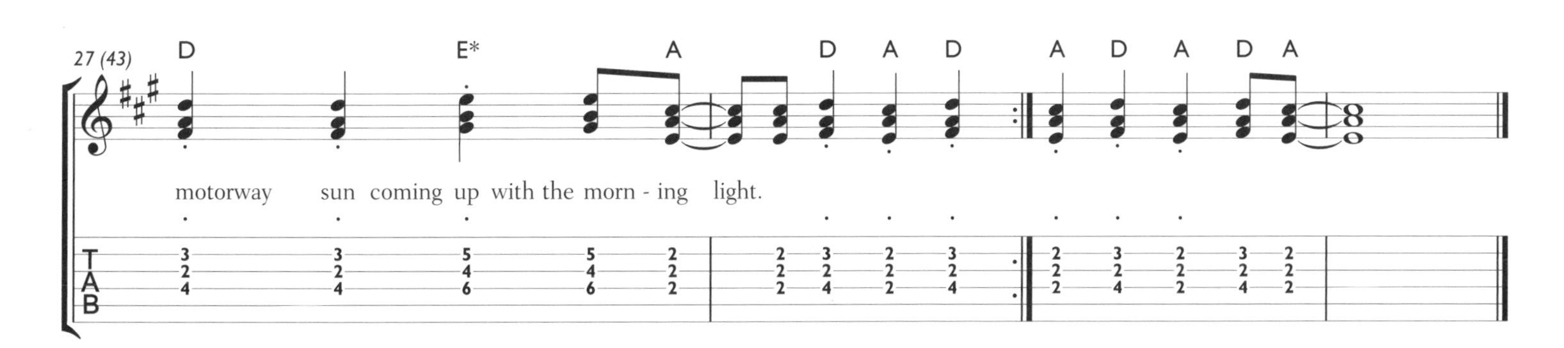
27 (43)
D
E*
A
D
A
D
A
D
A
D
A
motorway sun coming up with the morn - ing light.
T
A
B

SONGS ROCK AROUND THE CLOCK

Bill Haley And His Comets
Words and Music by Max C. Freedman and Jimmy De Knight

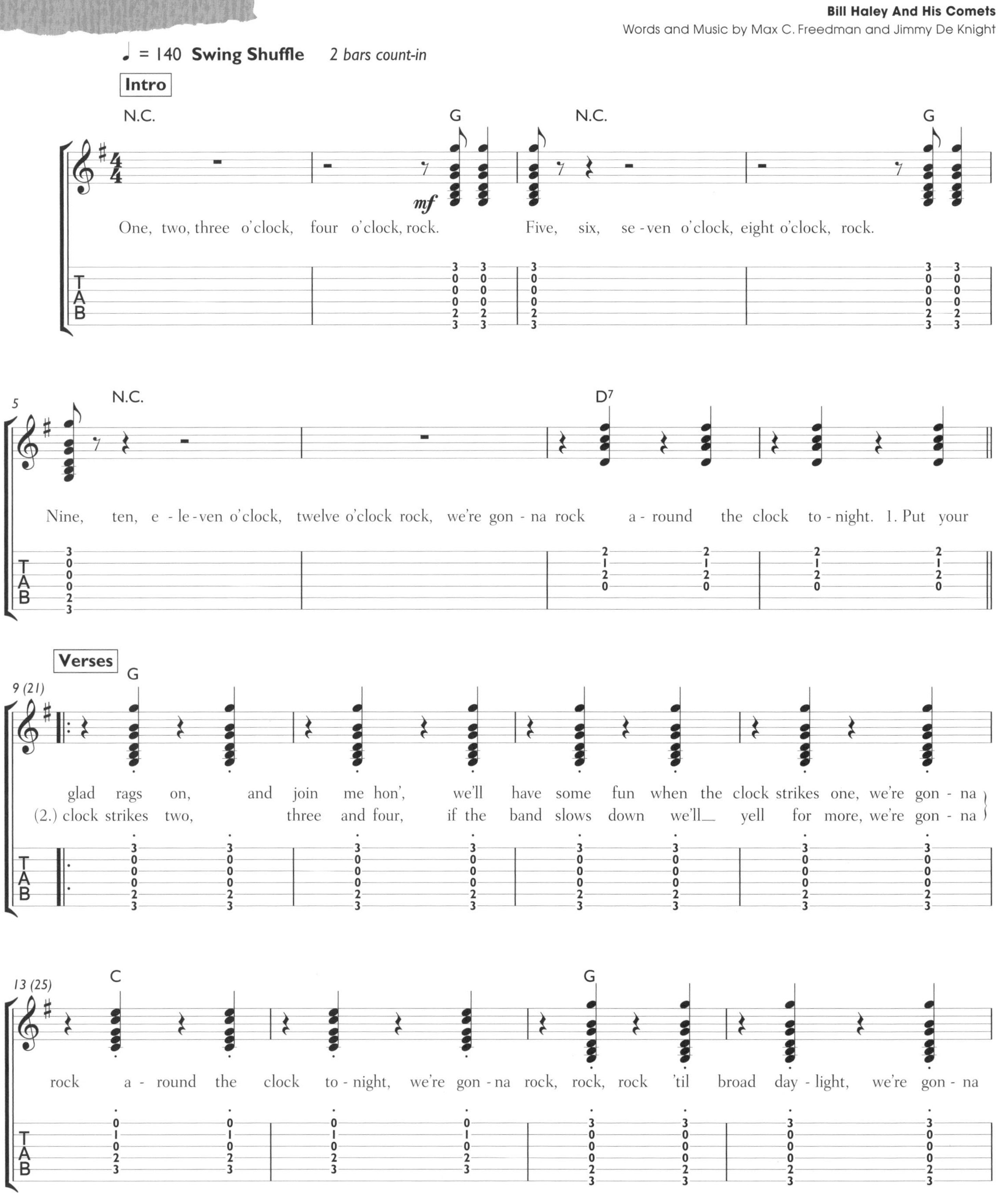

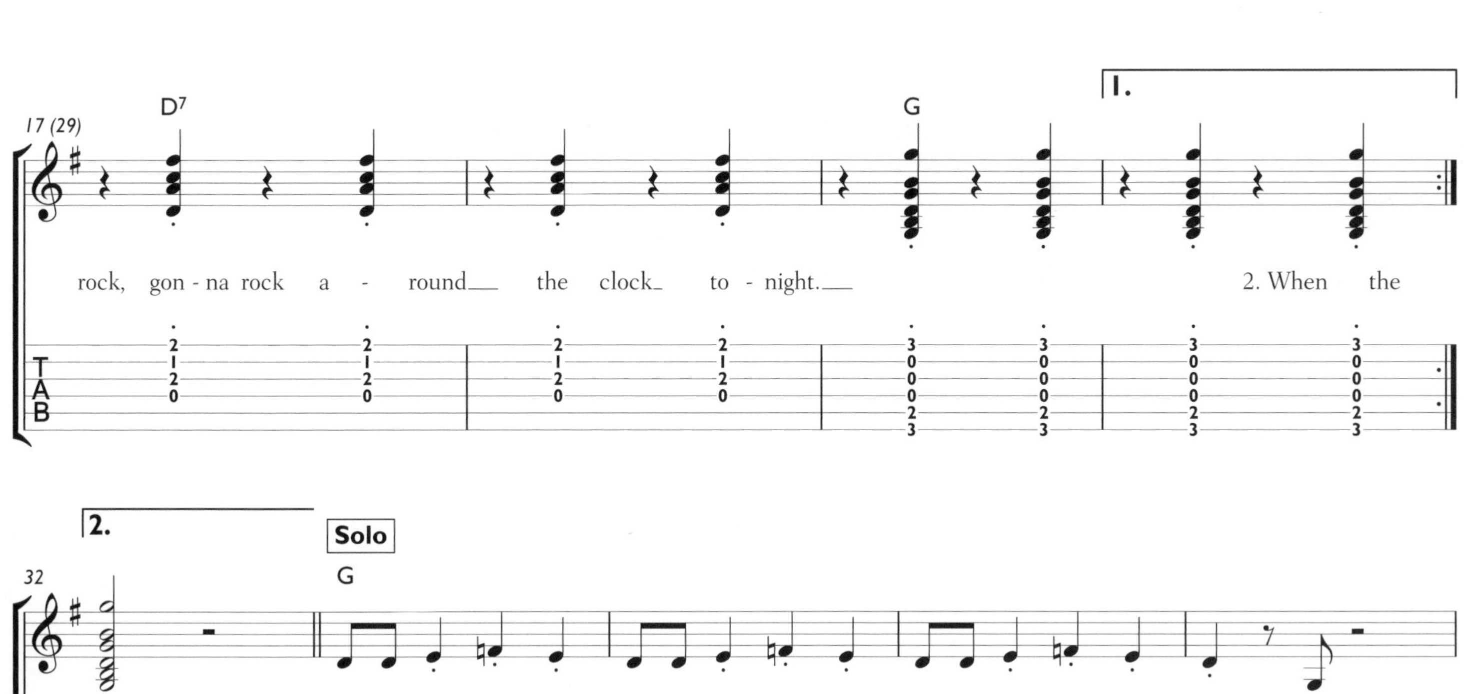
17 (29)
D7
G
1.
rock, gon - na rock a - round the clock to - night.
2. When the

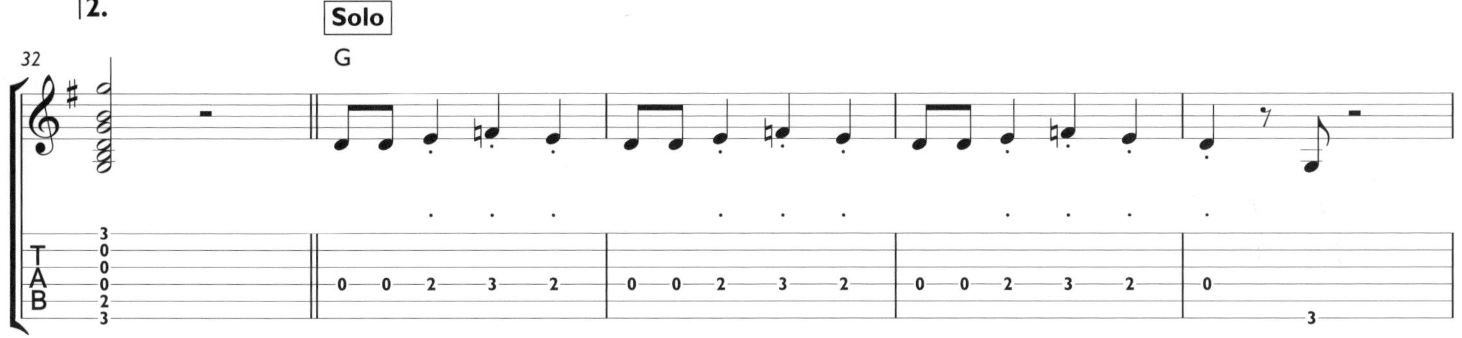
2.
Solo
32
G

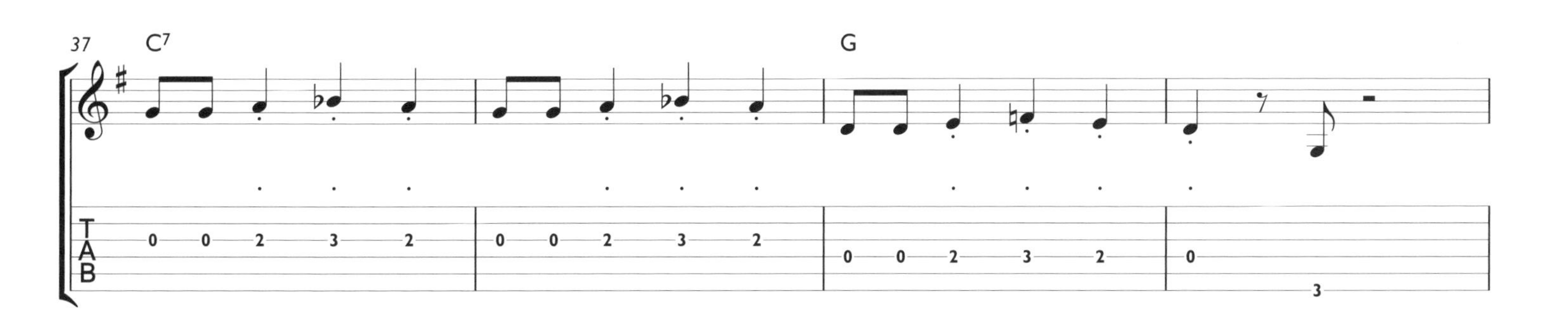
37
C7
G

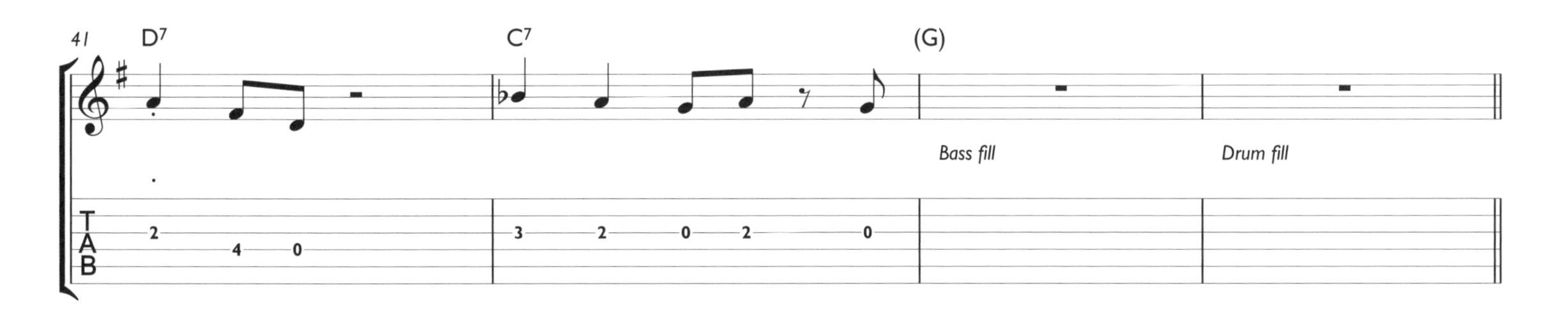
41
D7
C7
(G)
Bass fill
Drum fill

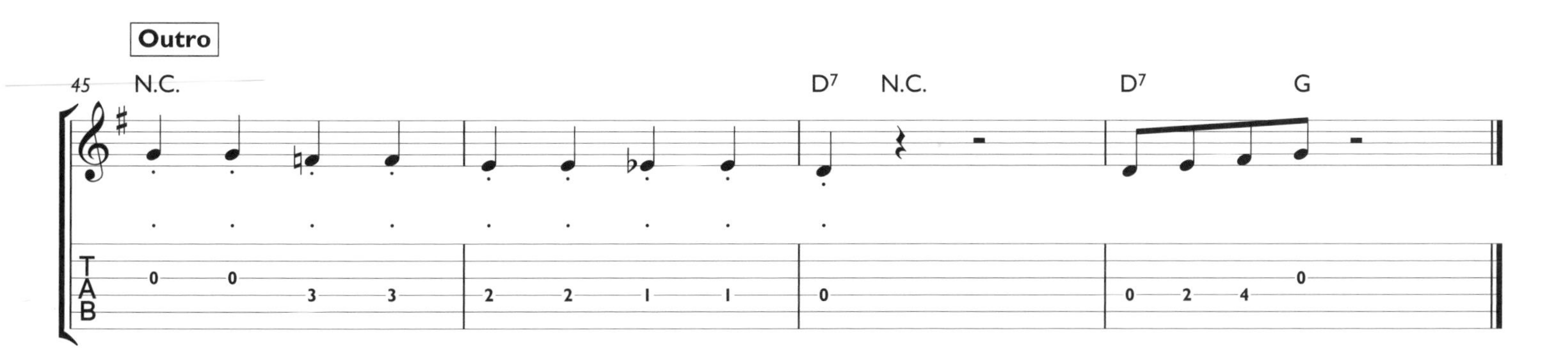
Outro
45
N.C.
D7
N.C.
D7
G

demo backing

SONGS PRETTY VACANT

Sex Pistols

Words and Music by Paul Cook, Glen Matlock, Steve Jones and Johnny Rotten

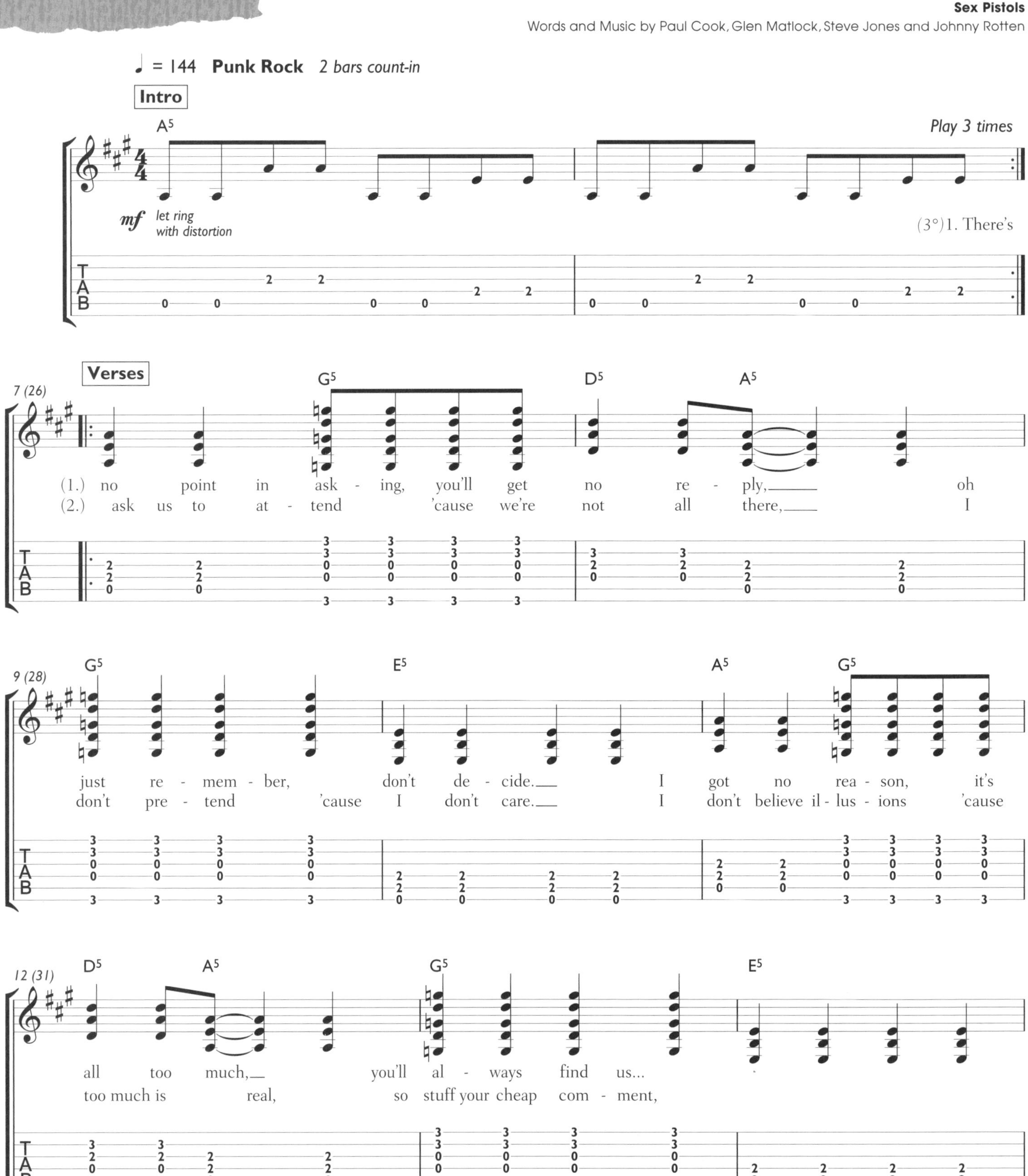

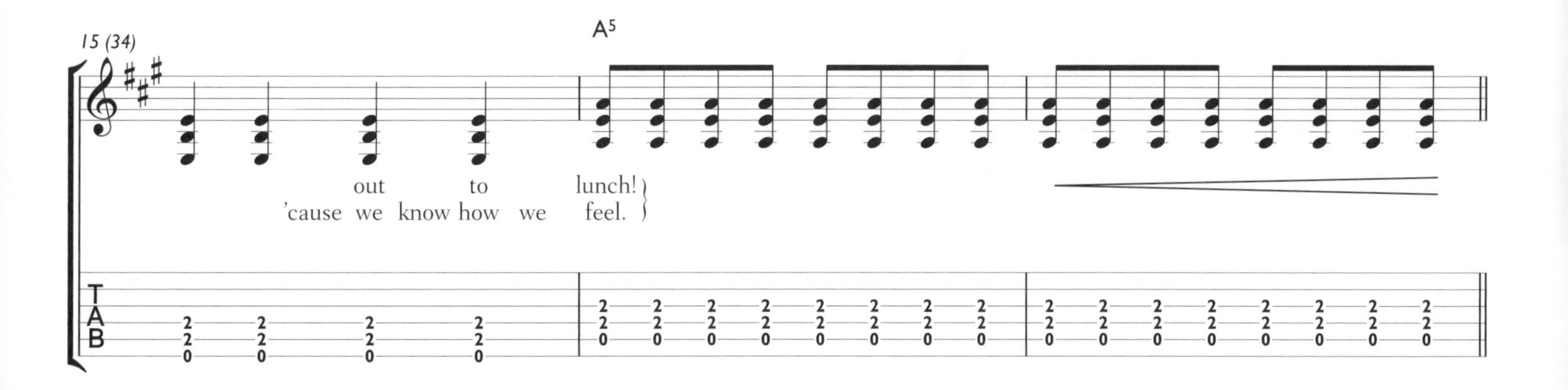
15 (34)
A5
out to lunch!
'cause we know how we feel.
TAB

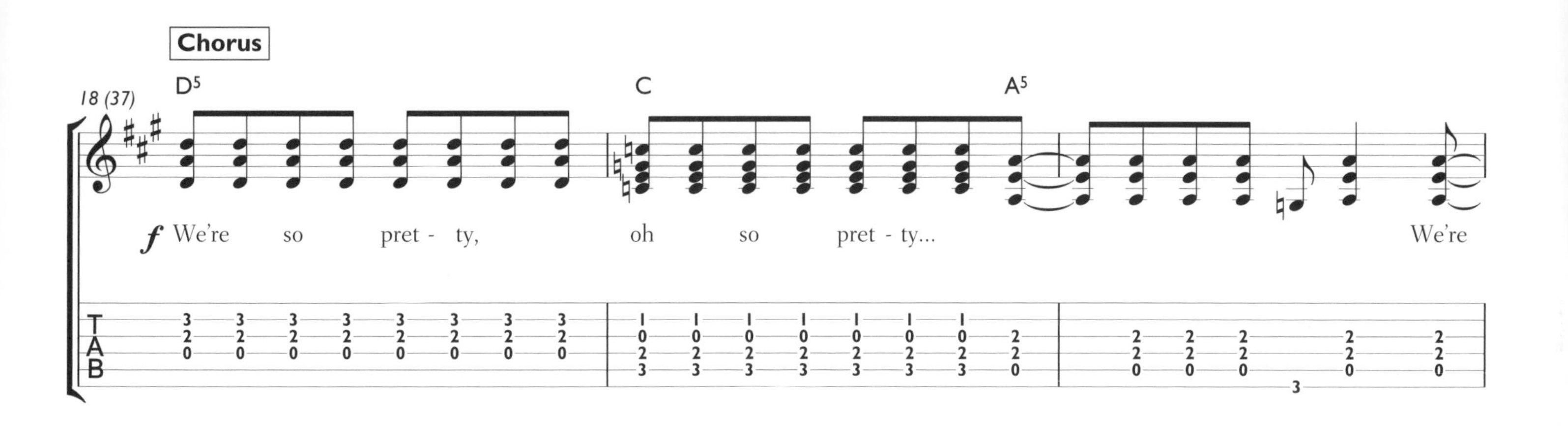
Chorus
18 (37)
D5
C
A5
f We're so pret - ty, oh so pret - ty... We're
TAB

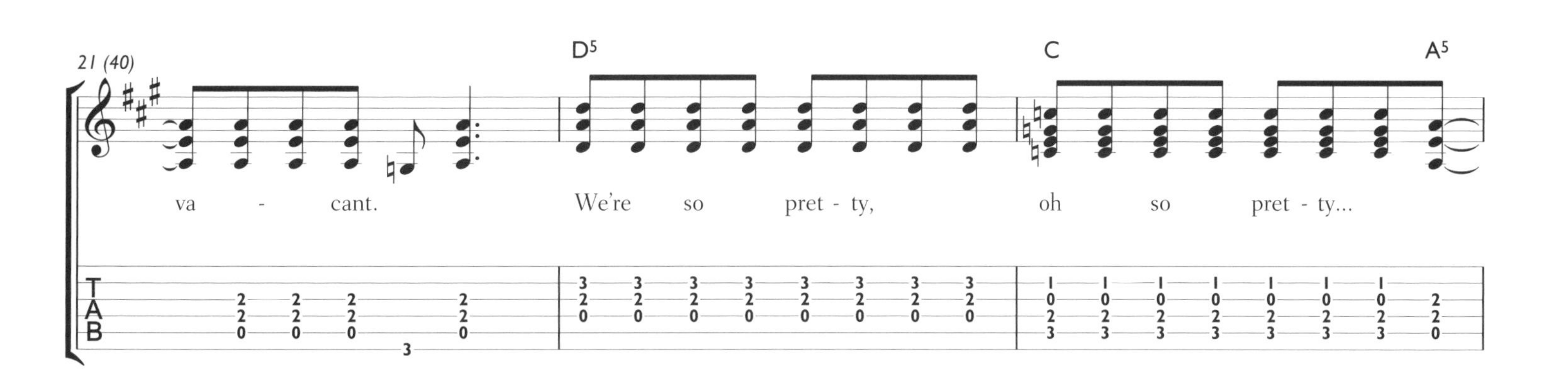
21 (40)
D5
C
A5
va - cant. We're so pret - ty, oh so pret - ty...
TAB

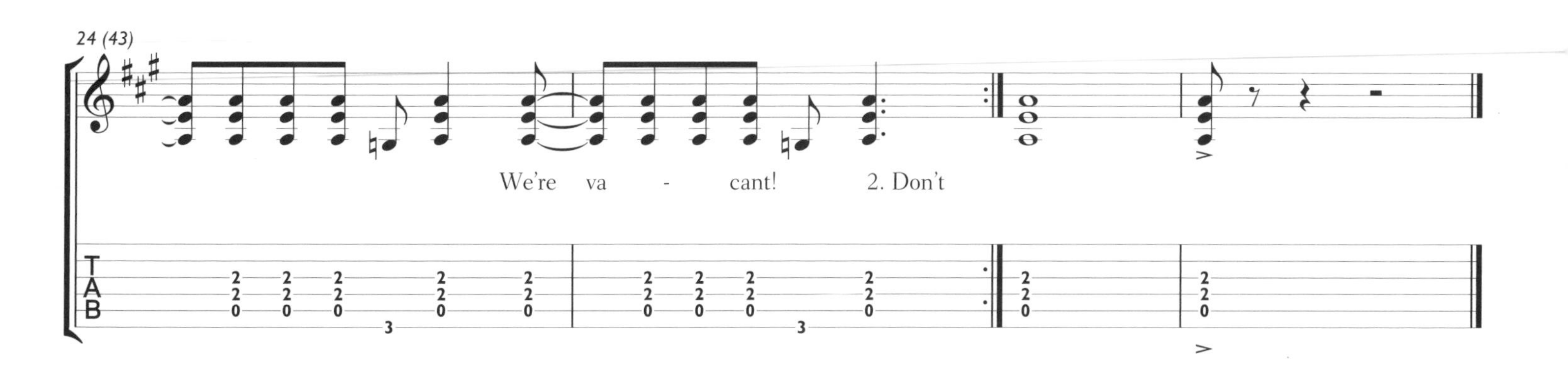
24 (43)
We're va - cant! 2. Don't
TAB

YOUR PAGE NOTES

TECHNICAL FOCUS

THE MODERN AGE

In your exam, you will be assessed on the following technical elements:

1 Crossed note-heads

Crossed note-heads on the beat indicate the use of right-hand damping to produce a sharp percussive 'chop' sound. These notes should be played using down-strokes, while the sounding off-beat chords should use up-strokes. This works best with:

- accurate timing
- clean damping
- consistent high energy.

2 Up-strokes and down-strokes

The verses, intro and outro all use an accented, syncopated chord pattern. These chords should only sound fully on the off-beat. Make each up-stroke chord sharp and aggressive.

In contrast, the chorus pattern should be played using only down-strokes. You will probably want to switch to this down-stroke pattern for the two-bar *crescendo* that leads into the chorus, but make sure that you keep the same energy level.

3 Chords

'The Modern Age' uses several different full chords including G^6 and $Dsus^2$.

- sus^2 chords have no third: the third of the chord is replaced by the second
- 6th chords are the same as major chords but with an added sixth.

Make sure that your chord changes are swift, accurate and strictly on the beat.

THE MODERN AGE

The Strokes

Words and Music by Julian Casablancas

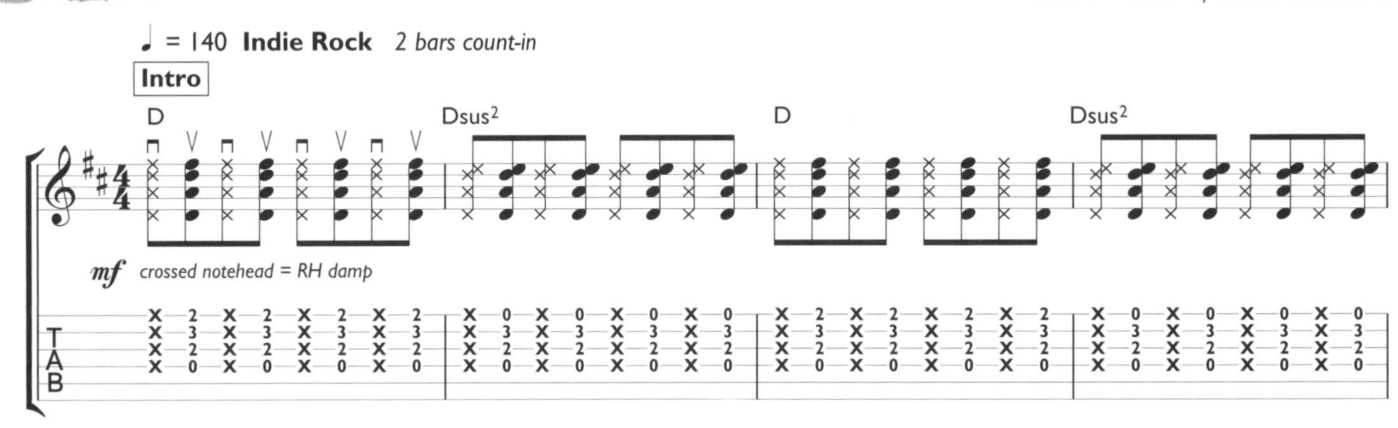

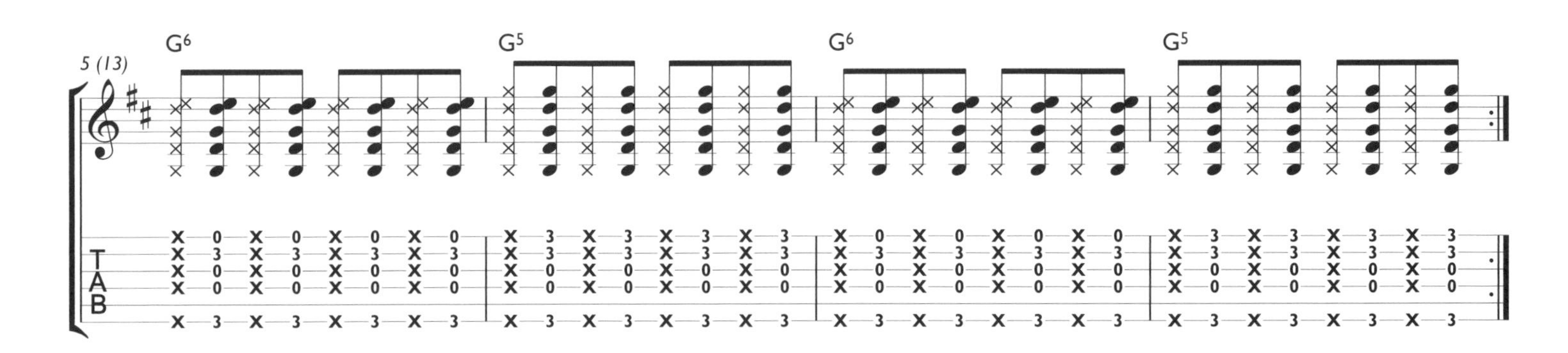

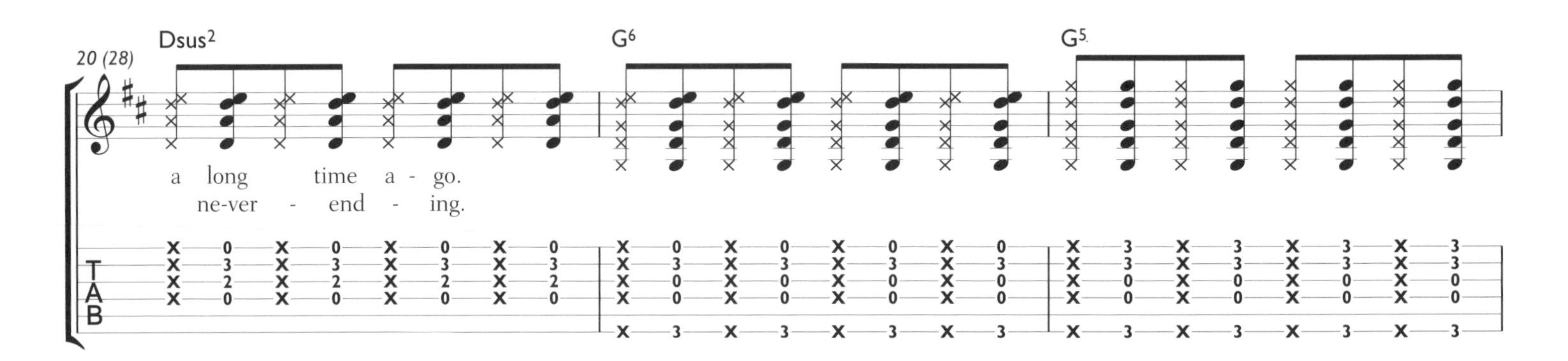

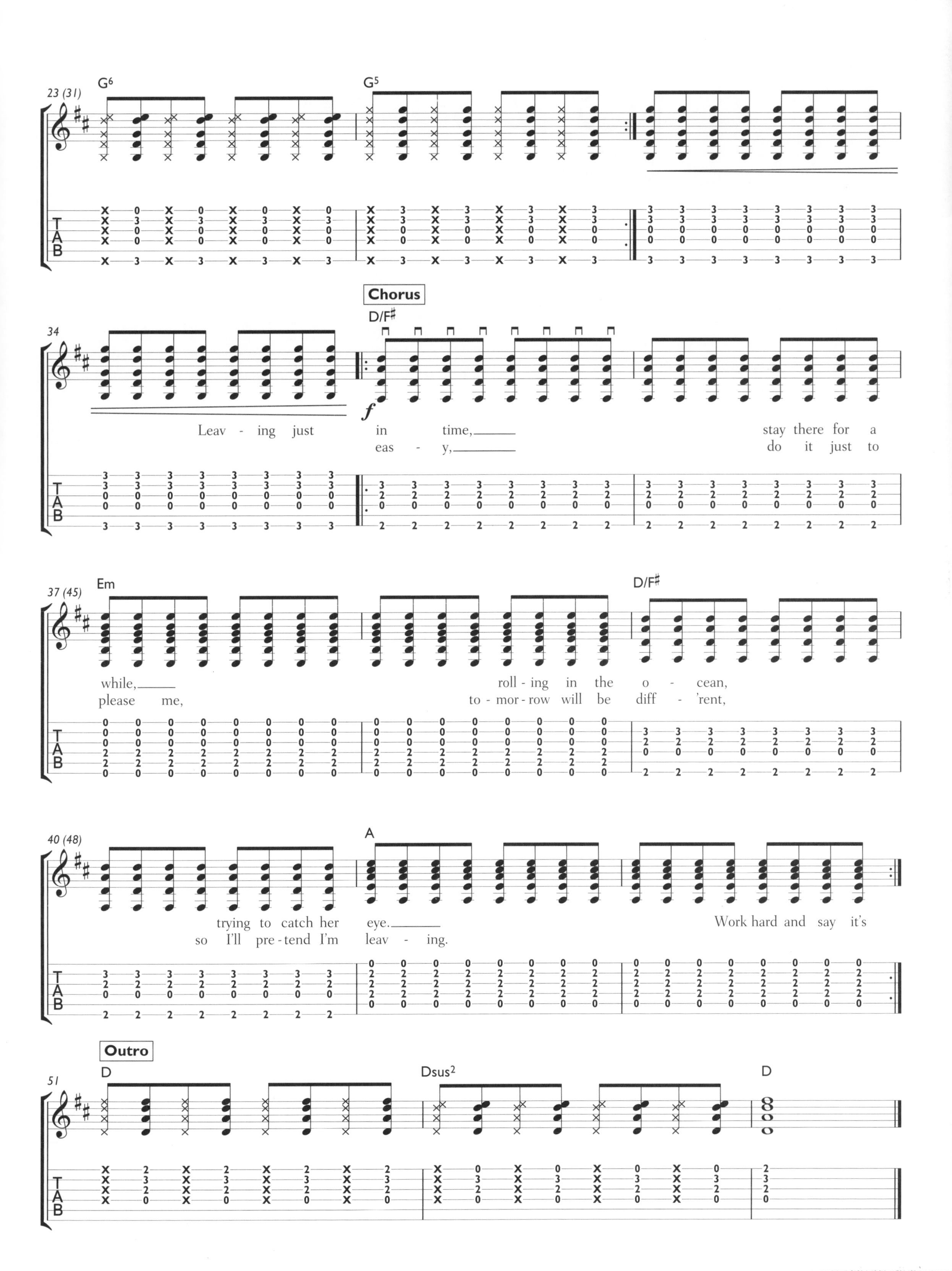
23 (31)
G6
G5
Chorus
34
D/F#
Leav - ing just in time,
eas - y,
stay there for a
do it just to
37 (45)
Em
D/F#
while,
please me,
roll - ing in the o - cean,
to - mor - row will be diff - 'rent,
40 (48)
A
trying to catch her eye.
so I'll pre - tend I'm leav - ing.
Work hard and say it's
Outro
51
D
Dsus2
D

YOUR PAGE NOTES

TECHNICAL FOCUS

MEAN JUMPER BLUES

In your exam, you will be assessed on the following technical elements:

1 Playing a riff

This minor blues is built around a simple low guitar riff. A riff is a phrase that is repeated many times throughout a song.

In bar 5, the riff is built over the chord of Am, with the added note G fretted at the third fret. In bar 9, the riff moves to Dm, with an added C, also fretted at the third fret.

When you are playing consecutive notes on adjacent strings, take care not to let one note ring on over the next. And do not allow notes to ring through the rests – particularly when playing open strings.

2 Full chords and power chords

The bridge section provides a contrast with the verse. When you play the full chords, they should be:

- spread slightly (marked by ⌇)
- clearly placed
- allowed to ring fully.

The G and Am power chords should be muted slightly. When you get to bar 34, the muting can be released to produce an effective *crescendo*.

3 Counting

'Mean Jumper Blues' does not start on the first beat of the bar but on the final ♪ – this is usually known as a 'pick up' (it is sometimes called an upbeat or *anacrusis*). The guitar riff at the beginning of the song starts on the pick-up note. Keep counting the beat and place this note accurately.

Count carefully on the long notes in bars 29–30 and 33. Make sure that you hold them on for the right length.

Near the end of the song – at bar 46 – there is an accented ♪ E^7 chord. The rest of this bar is silent so you will need to count **1** 2 3 4 to make sure that you come in at the right place at the beginning of bar 47.

BAND OPTION

MEAN JUMPER BLUES

Blind Lemon Jefferson
Words and Music by Blind Lemon Jefferson

♩ = 90 **Blues** *2 bars count-in*

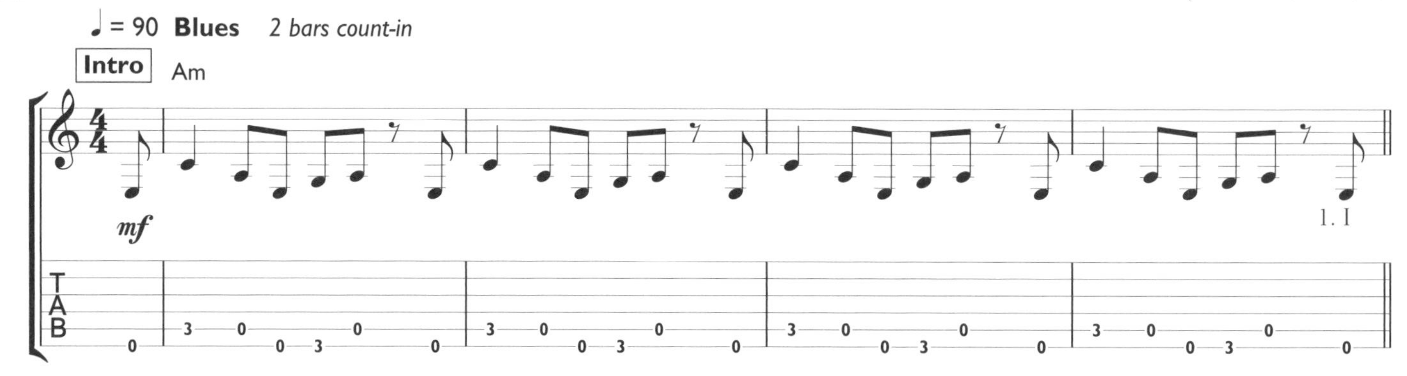

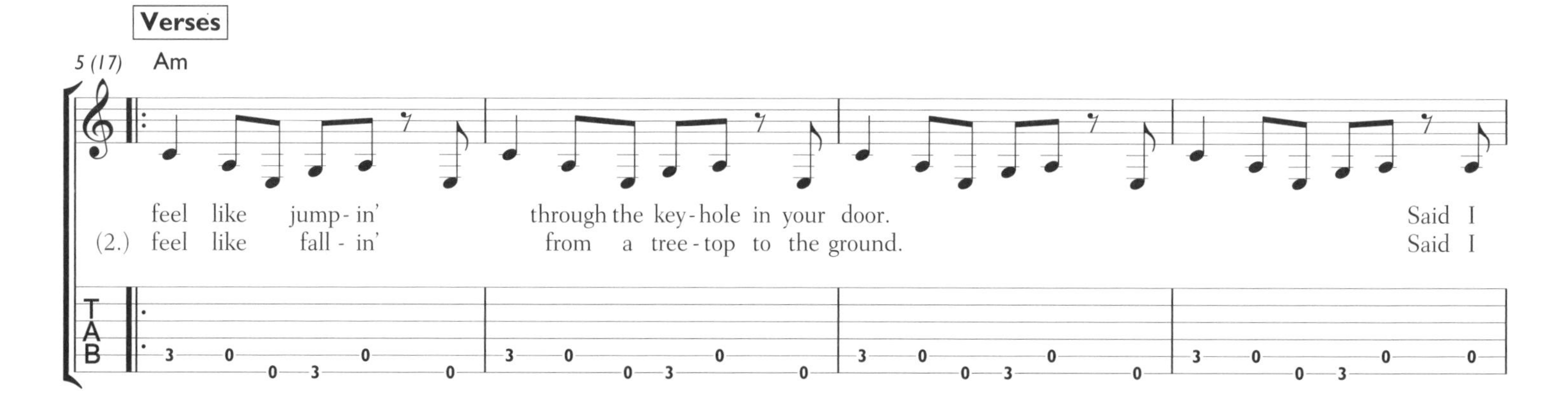

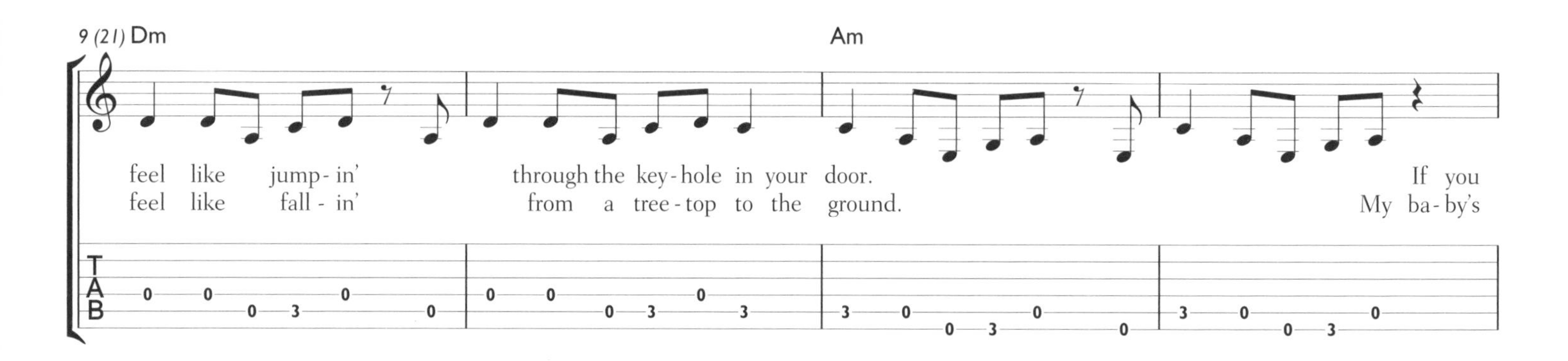

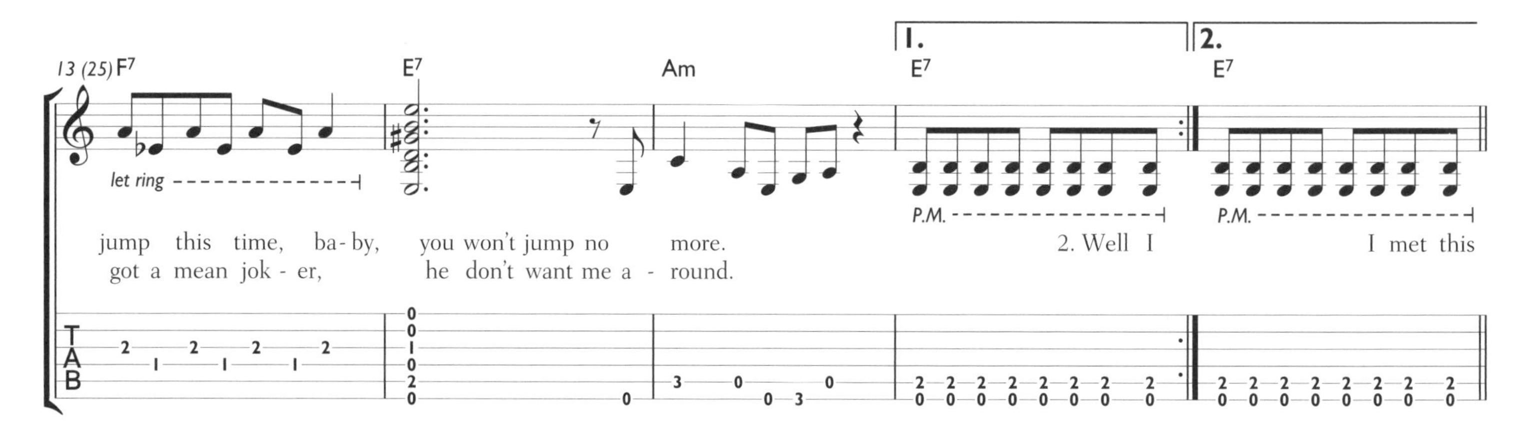

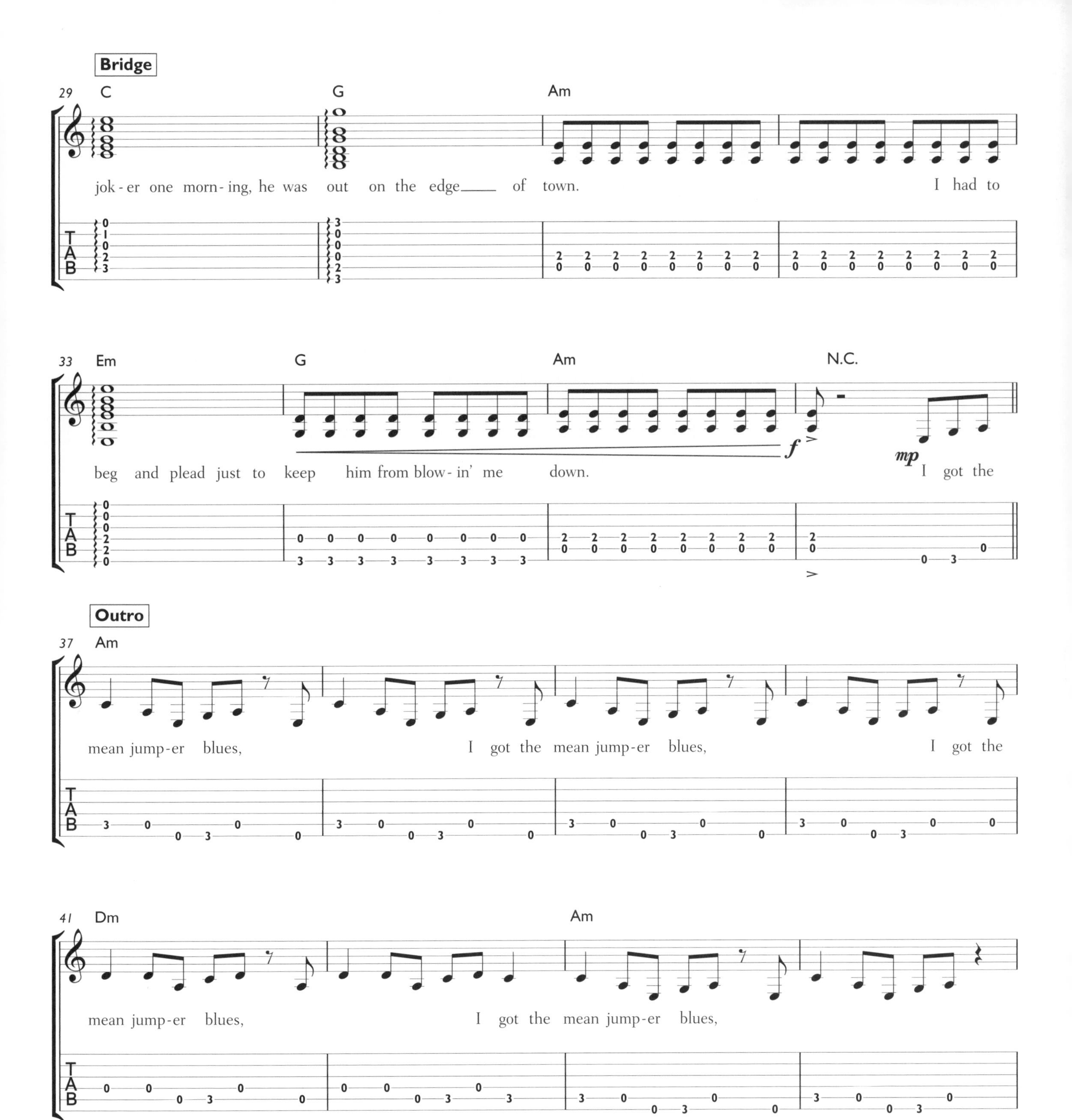
Bridge
29
C
G
Am
jok - er one morn - ing, he was out on the edge of town. I had to
33
Em
G
Am
N.C.
f
mp
beg and plead just to keep him from blow - in' me down. I got the
Outro
37
Am
mean jump - er blues, I got the mean jump - er blues, I got the
41
Dm
Am
mean jump - er blues, I got the mean jump - er blues,

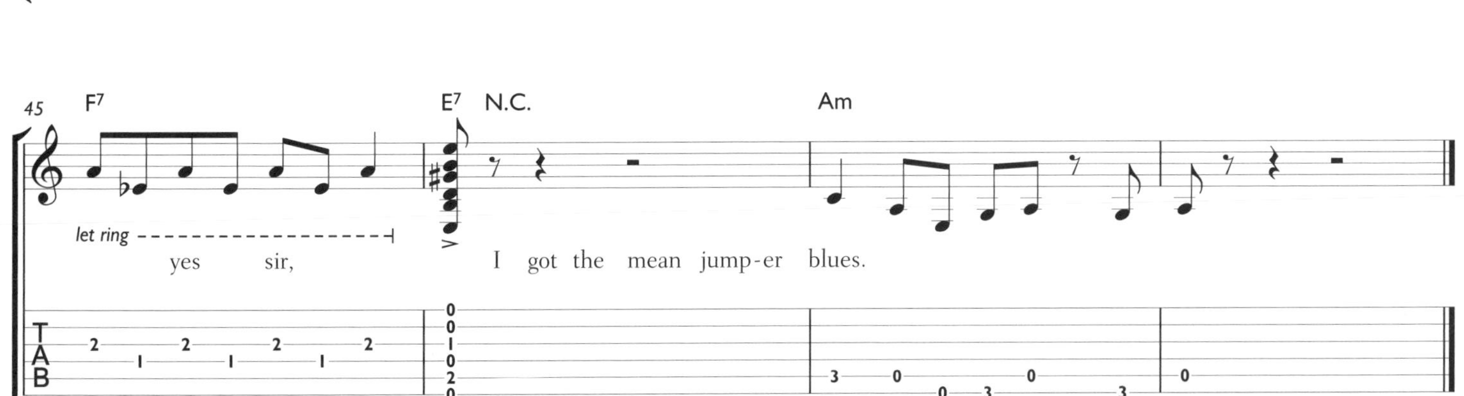
45
F7
E7
N.C.
Am
let ring
yes sir, I got the mean jump - er blues.

ABOUT THE SONGS

I LOVE ROCK 'N' ROLL

Joan Jett And The Blackhearts

Joan Jett (born Joan Larkin, in 1960) formed her first band when she was 15 – an all-girl group of Los Angeles teenagers called the Runaways. When the band split, she moved to New York and formed Joan Jett And The Blackhearts. It was not long before they had a No. 1 hit with 'I Love Rock'n'Roll', a raucous guitar rock cover of an obscure B-side by the English band The Arrows.

Like many other female rock singers, Joan Jett was inspired by the leather-clad Suzi Quatro – a bass player and lead singer who had her own successful rock band in the 1970s.

'I Love Rock'n'Roll' is built around three power chords: E^5, A^5 and B^5. Power chords are made up of only the root and the 5th of the chord, giving a more open and powerful sound. They are very common in rock music. The ♩♪♩ chords should be played using only down-strokes.

The phrase at the end of bars 6 and 8 should be played using a combination of down-strokes (⊓) and up-strokes (V) – as shown in bar 6. Give the last note of the run (G) an extra 'push' or accent.

The time signature changes during this song. Most of it is in $\frac{4}{4}$, but bar 12 is in $\frac{2}{4}$. Think of it as a half bar and, when you are counting, make sure you begin counting in four again from bar 13. Similarly, bar 21 (25 on repeat) is in $\frac{3}{4}$, so make sure you count three for this bar.

'I could *tell* it *wouldn't* be long *til he* was *with* me'

ABOUT THE SONGS

2,4,6,8 MOTORWAY

Tom Robinson Band

Tom Robinson, the singer, songwriter and bassist formed a punk band – the Tom Robinson Band – in 1976. Their single, '2, 4, 6, 8 Motorway', was released in 1977 – a raucous sing-along number which became an immediate hit. In 1978, the song was included on the band's first album, *Power In The Darkness*.

Tom Robinson has been a political activist throughout his life – many of his songs have political themes and he was a leader of the Rock Against Racism campaign. He now works mainly as a BBC radio presenter.

The guitar part uses only the D, G and B strings for the whole of '2, 4, 6, 8 Motorway'. Be careful not to let the other open strings sound.

This song uses these chord shapes:

- the A shape – play this using the first finger to barre across all three strings
- this barre stays in place for the D chord – add the second and third fingers on the B and D strings. Practise moving between the A and D chords until you can change smoothly
- the E* shape in bar 7 is achieved by moving the D shape two frets higher up the fret board, while the E shape in bar 5 can be thought of as being part of a full first position open E chord.

The ♩ chords are all marked *staccato*. Play these notes short and detached.

Most of '2, 4, 6, 8 Motorway' is played ***mf*** (moderately loud) but the chorus is marked ***f*** (loud). Make sure there is a contrast between the two sections.

'Whizz-kid *sitting* pretty *on* your *two-wheel* stallion'

ABOUT THE SONGS

ROCK AROUND THE CLOCK

Bill Haley And His Comets

This Bill Haley And His Comets song was, for many people, the first rock 'n' roll music that they heard. It is hard to imagine the far-reaching and powerful effect that it had on its audience.

The use of 'Rock Around The Clock' on the soundtrack of the 1955 film *Blackboard Jungle* helped to cement the association of rock 'n' roll with teenage rebellion and when, a year later, the film *Rock Around The Clock* was released in cinemas across the United States and Europe, it caused a sensation. Audiences were dancing in the aisles and out on the streets and there were unruly, sometimes violent scenes. In some places the film was banned and rock 'n' roll was denounced from the pulpit.

The raw and punchy song became a symbol of the teenage generation and soon sold millions of copies.

Count carefully to make sure that you enter at the right point in the intro. The vocal cue should also help you. The guitar plays the same rhythm after both of the first two vocal entries. These chords should be strummed up-down-down.

The guitar plays on the off-beats throughout the verse. All these chords can be played as down-strokes. They are all marked *staccato*: play them short and detached. *Staccato* is also used in the guitar solo and outro.

'*We'll* have *some* fun *when* the *clock* strikes *one*'

ABOUT THE SONGS

PRETTY VACANT

Sex Pistols

This punk rock classic was released as a single in 1977. It has many of the characteristics of punk music – short and energetic, with angry abrasive lyrics, a simple chord progression and a raw, chaotic sound, heavy with distortion. Johnny Rotten's trademark sneering voice with its raucous half-shouting style of singing has been much copied, and the Sex Pistols' style has inspired countless bands.

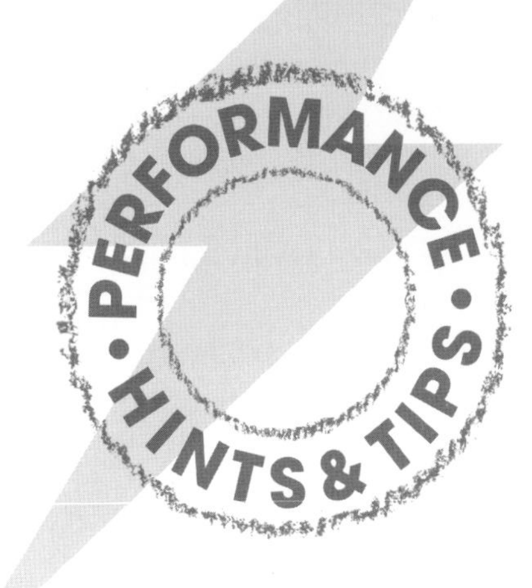

The intro pattern in 'Pretty Vacant' does not need any left-hand movement (a three-note A^5 power chord is held throughout), but you do need some right-hand dexterity, particularly when skipping between the A string and the G string.

Use down-strokes on the beat, up-strokes on the off-beat throughout the song. This should result in fluid rhythms with plenty of energy.

Be careful not to play a standard D major chord in place of the D^5 chord. Make sure the open top E string does not sound.

'I don't *believe illusions* 'cause *too* much *is* real'

ABOUT THE SONGS

THE MODERN AGE

The Strokes

The Strokes, a New York indie rock band, released 'The Modern Age' in 2001. It was one of three songs on their debut EP *The Modern Age* and became an instant hit on both sides of the Atlantic. With its rough edgy sound, driving guitars and distorted vocals, this song could be described as garage rock.

Three of the band's five members began playing together when they were at school in New York. Although they are an American band, 'The Modern Age' was first released on the famous UK indie label Rough Trade.

This song uses the same rhythm throughout. Focus on playing in time with the drums.

Most of the song should be played ***mf*** (*mezzo forte* = moderately loud) with a *crescendo* to ***f*** (*forte* = loud) for the chorus. Make a clear difference between the two dynamics.

Be ready for all of the repeat marks – make sure you know where to repeat back to.

ABOUT THE SONGS

MEAN JUMPER BLUES

Blind Lemon Jefferson

'Mean Jumper Blues' is a 12-bar blues song first recorded by the Texan blues singer and guitarist Blind Lemon Jefferson. Like most blues (early American black music originally performed by one singer accompanied on guitar or banjo), 'Mean Jumper Blues' has four beats in a bar and is built around a three-line verse, where the second line is a repeat of the first.

As a young man, Blind Lemon Jefferson was a poverty-stricken wandering street musician. Despite this, he built up a good reputation and, in 1925, became one of the first country blues musicians to get a recording contract. These early recordings went on to have a big influence on rock musicians. Many artists have covered his songs, including Bob Dylan, Grateful Dead and Counting Crows. Blind Lemon Jefferson froze to death in 1929 during a snow storm, having had a heart attack.

'Mean Jumper Blues' is marked ***mf*** (*mezzo forte*) for most of the song, so you should play it quite quietly. There is a big *crescendo*, marked by a < at bars 34–35. In these bars, you should get gradually louder – play each chord louder than the one before – and then drop straight down to ***mp*** at the end of bar 36.

Watch out for the G♯ accidentals.

P.M. in bars 16 and 29 stands for 'palm muting', which means you should slightly mute the sound by touching the heel of your hand against the strings.

This song is also in the vocals, keyboards, bass and drums books, so you can get together and play it in a band.

'If you jump this time, baby, you won't jump no more'

SESSION SKILLS

PLAYBACK

For your exam, you can choose either Playback or Improvising (see page 28). If you choose Playback, you will be asked to play some music you have not seen or heard before.

In the exam, you will be given the song chart and the examiner will play a recording of the music. You will hear several two-bar phrases on the recording: you should play each of them straight back in turn. There's a rhythm track going throughout, which helps you keep in time. There should not be any gaps in the music.

In the exam you will have two chances to play with the recording:

- First time – for practice
- Second time – for assessment.

You should listen to the audio, copying what you hear; you can also read the music from the song chart. Here are some practice song charts which are also on the CD in this book.

Don't forget that the Playback test can include requirements which may not be shown in these examples, including those from earlier grades. Check the parameters at www.trinityrock.com to prepare for everything which might come up in your exam.

'*I* really *like* the *way* music *looks* on *paper.* It *looks* like *art* to *me*'

Steve Vai

Practice playback 1

♩ = 120

Practice playback 2

♩ = 118

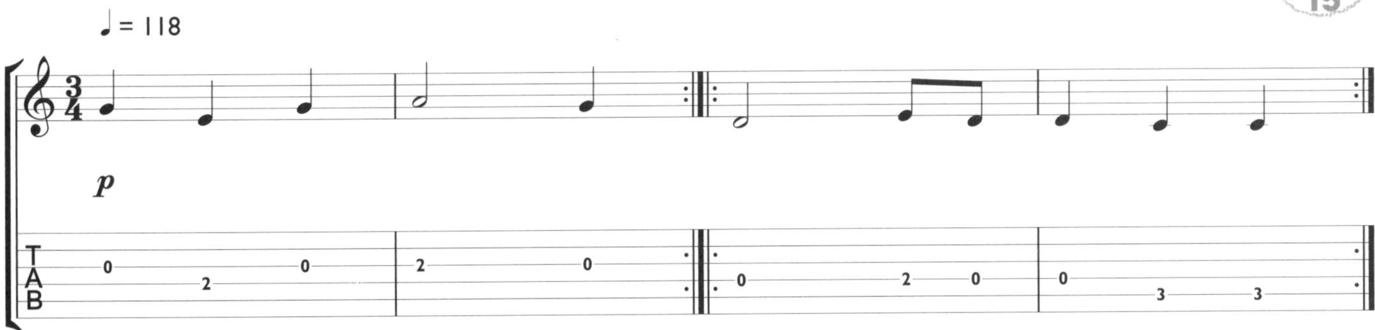

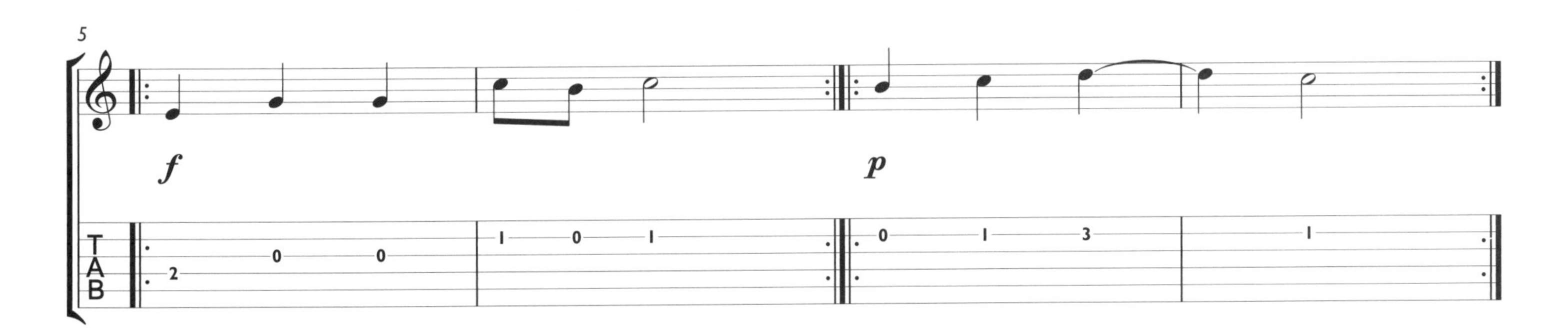

SESSION SKILLS IMPROVISING

For your exam, you can choose either Playback (see page 26), or Improvising. If you choose to improvise, you will be asked to improvise over a backing track that you haven't heard before in a specified style.

In the exam, you will be given a song chart and the examiner will play a recording of the backing track. The backing track consists of a passage of music played on a loop. You should improvise a lead melodic line or rhythmic chords over it.

In the exam you will have two chances to play with the recording:

- First time – for practice
- Second time – for assessment.

Here are some practice improvisation charts which are also on the CD in this book.

Don't forget that the Improvising test can include requirements which may not be shown in these examples, including those from earlier grades. Check the parameters at www.trinityrock.com to prepare for everything which might come up in your exam.

Practice improvisation 1

♩ = 120 **Rock**

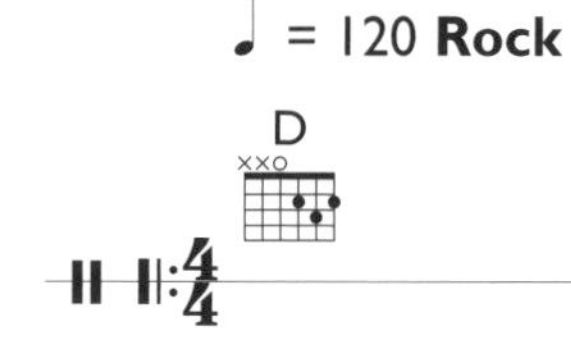

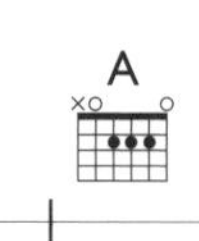

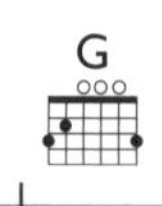

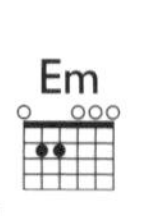

Practice improvisation 2

♩ = 100 **Country**

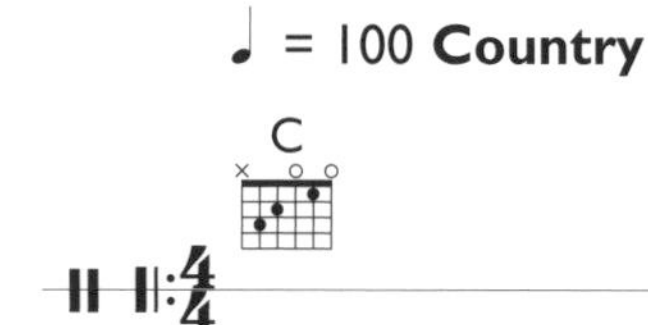

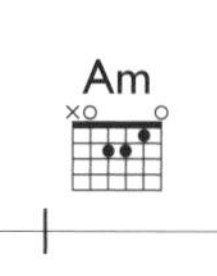

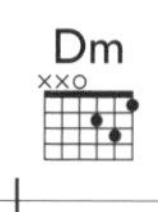

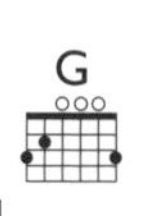

HELP PAGES

CHOOSING A SONG FOR YOUR EXAM

There are lots of options to help you choose your three songs for the exam.
For Songs 1 and 2, you can choose a song which is:

- from this book
- from www.trinityrock.com

Or for Song 2 you can choose a song which is:

- sheet music from a printed or online source
- your own arrangement of a song or a song you have written yourself (see page 30).

You can play the song unaccompanied or with a backing track (minus the solo instrument). If you like, you can create a backing track yourself (or with friends), or you could add your own vocals – or both.

For Grade 2, the song should last between one and three-and-a-half minutes, and the level of difficulty should be similar to your other songs. When choosing a song, think about:

- Does it work on my instrument?
- Are there any technical elements that are too difficult for me? (If so, perhaps save it for when you do the next grade.)
- Do I enjoy playing it?
- Does it work with my other pieces to create a good set-list?

See www.trinityrock.com for further information and advice on choosing your own song.

SHEET MUSIC

You must always bring an original copy of the book or a download sheet with email certificate for each song you perform in the exam. If you choose to write your own song you must provide the examiner with a copy of the sheet music.
Your music can be:

- a lead sheet with lyrics, chords and melody line
- a chord chart with lyrics
- a full score using conventional staff/TAB notation
- see page 30 for details on presenting a song you have written yourself.

The title of the song and your name should be on the sheet music.

HELP PAGES

WRITING YOUR OWN SONG

You can play a song that you have written yourself for one of the choices in your exam. For Grade 2, your song should last between one minute and three and a half minutes, so it is likely to be quite straightforward. It is sometimes difficult to know where to begin, however. Here are some suggestions for starting points:

- **A melody**: many songs are made up around a 'hook' (a short catchy melodic idea, usually only a few notes long).

Try writing a couple of ideas for hooks here:

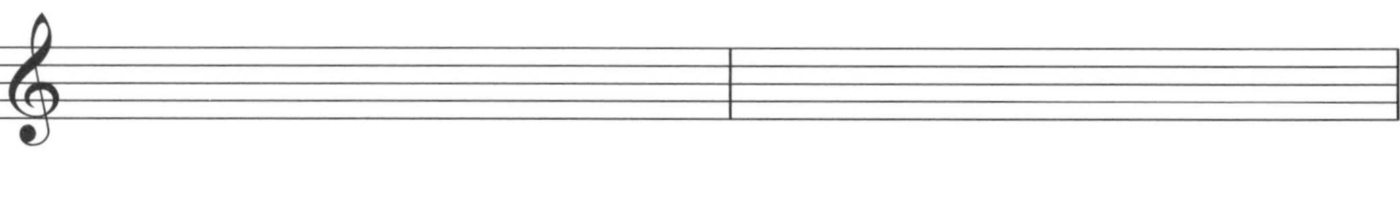

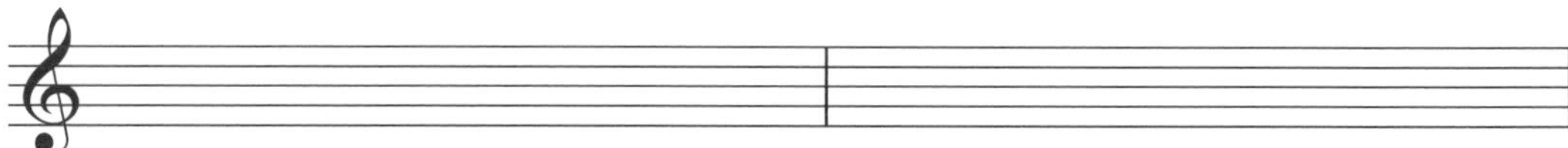

- **A riff**: A riff is a very short melodic or rhythmic idea which is repeated over and over. It often underpins an entire song. Write a couple of short riffs here:

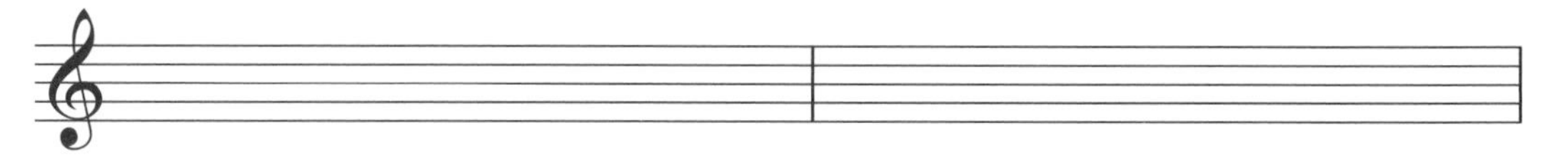

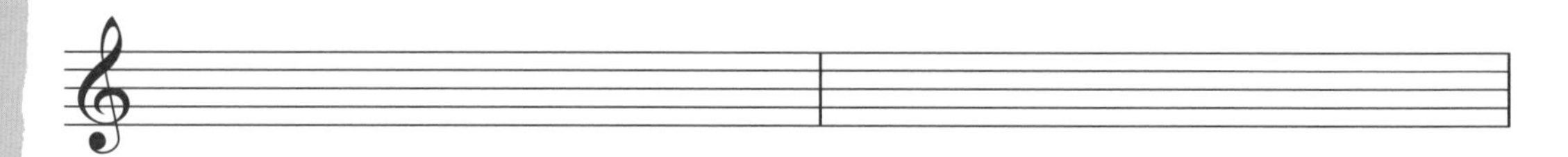

- **A word or phrase, theme or subject**: certain words and subjects suggest particular styles of music: a song about riding a motorbike might have a driving rhythm, a love song could be more reflective.

There are plenty of other ways of starting: perhaps with a chord sequence or a lyric, for example.

You will also need to consider the **structure** of your song (verse and chorus, 12-bar blues, and so on), the **style** it is in (blues, hard rock, etc.), and what **instruments** it is for (solo guitar or voice/guitar/keyboards/drums . . .).

There are many choices to be made – which is why writing a song is such a rewarding thing to do.

WRITING YOUR SONG DOWN

Rock and pop music is often written as a **lead sheet** with the lyrics (if there are any), chords and a melody line.

- As a guitar player, you may want to write your part on a **five-line stave** or as **tab**. Both have been used for the songs in this book.
- You can, if you prefer, use a **graph** or **table** to represent your music, as long as it is clear to anyone else (including the examiner) how the song goes.

HELP PAGES

PLAYING IN A BAND

Playing in a band is exciting: it can be a lot of fun and, as with everything, the more you do it, the easier it gets. It is very different from playing on your own. Everyone contributes to the overall sound: the most important skill you need to develop is listening.

For a band to sound good, the players need to be 'together' – that mainly means keeping in time with each other, but also playing at the same volume, and with the same kind of feeling.

Your relationship with the other band members is also important. Talk with them about the music you play, the music you like, and what you'd like the band to achieve short-term and long-term.

Band rehearsals are important – you should not be late, tired or distracted by your mobile phone! Being positive makes a huge difference. Try to create a friendly atmosphere in rehearsals so that everybody feels comfortable trying out new things. Don't worry about making mistakes: that is what rehearsals are for.

'Mean Jumper Blues' (page 18) is arranged for band. You will find parts for vocals, keyboards, bass and drums in the other Trinity Rock & Pop Grade 2 books. There are also parts for 'Rock Around The Clock' in the Trinity Rock & Pop Grade 2 Drums and Bass books. Trinity offers exams for groups of musicians at various levels. The songs arranged for bands are ideal to include as part of a set-list for these exams. Have a look at the website for more details.

HINTS AND TIPS

- Your own ability as a musician is important – if you have practised different techniques on your own, then you will have more to offer to the band. It is worth remembering that simple parts can be very effective, it is not always necessary for each instrument to play every note in the chord, or on every beat of the bar.
- If you have two guitars, try and make the sound of each guitar different. It can sound clearer if the guitars play different parts or in different styles.
- Some instruments could stop playing in certain sections. This is a very effective way of increasing the range of dynamics.

HELP PAGES

PLAYING WITH BACKING TRACKS

The CD contains demos and backing tracks of all the songs in the book. The additional songs at www.trinityrock.com also come with demos and backing tracks.

- In your exam, you should play with the backing track, or you can create your own (see below).
- The backing tracks start with a click track, which sets the tempo and helps you start accurately.
- Be careful to set the balance between the volume of the backing track and your instrument.
- Listen carefully to the backing track to ensure you are playing in time.

If you are creating your own backing track here are some further tips:

- Make sure the sound quality is of a good standard.
- Think carefully about the instruments/sounds you are putting on the backing track.
- Avoid copying what you are playing on the backing track – it should support not duplicate.
- Do you need to include a click track at the beginning?

COPYRIGHT IN A SONG

If you are a singer or songwriter it is important to know about copyright. When someone writes a song or creates an arrangement they own the copyright (sometimes called 'the rights') to that version. The copyright means that other people cannot copy it, sell it, perform it in a concert, make it available online or record it without the owner's permission or the appropriate licence. When you write a song you automatically own the copyright to it, which means that other people cannot copy your work. But just as importantly, you cannot copy other people's work, or perform it in public without their permission or the appropriate licence.

Points to remember

- You can create a cover version of a song for an exam or other non-public performance.
- You cannot record your cover version and make your recording available to others (by copying it or uploading it to a website) without the appropriate licence.
- You own the copyright of your own original song, which means that no one is allowed to copy it.
- You cannot copy someone else's song without their permission or the appropriate licence.
- If you would like to use somebody else's words in your own song you must check if they are in copyright and, if so, we recommend you confirm with the author that they are happy for the words to be used as lyrics.
- Materials protected by copyright can normally be used as lyrics in our exams as these are private performances under copyright law. The examiner may ask you the name of the original author in the exam.
- When you present your own song to the examiner make sure you include the title, the names of any writers and the source of your lyrics.